DRACULA

a symphony in moonlight and nightmares

words and pictures	Jon J Muth
editor	Ann Nocenti
consulting editor	Margaret Clark
assistant editors	Terry Kavanagh
	Daniel Chichester
editor in chief	Jim Shooter

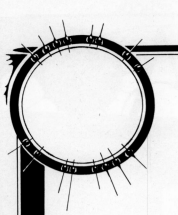

OTHER GRAPHIC NOVELS
FROM MARVEL® AND EPIC COMICS

Death of Captain Marvel ● Jim Starlin
Elric ● Roy Thomas & P. Craig Russell
Dreadstar ● Jim Starlin
The New Mutants ● Chris Claremont & Bob McLeod
The X-Men ● Chris Claremont & Brent Anderson
Star Slammers ● Walt Simonson
Killraven ● Don McGregor & P. Craig Russell
Super Boxers ● Ron Wilson with John Byrne & Armando Gil
Futurians ● Dave Cockrum
Heartburst ● Rick Veitch
Void Indigo ● Steve Gerber & Val Mayerick
Dazzler: The Movie ● Jim Shooter, Frank Springer & Vince Colletta
Starstruck ● Elaine Lee & Michael Wm. Kaluta
Swords of the Swashbucklers ● Bill Mantlo & Jackson Guice
The Raven Banner ● Alan Zelenetz & Charles Vess
The Aladdin Effect ● Jim Shooter, David Michelinie,
Greg LaRocque & Vince Colletta
Revenge of the Living Monolith ● David Michelinie,
Marc Silvestri & Geof Isherwood
The Sensational She-Hulk ● John Byrne with Kim DeMulder &
Petra Scotese
Conan the Barbarian in The Witch Queen of Acheron ● Don Kraar,
Gary Kwapisz & Art Nichols
Greenberg the Vampire ● J.M. DeMatteis & Mark Badger
Marada the She-Wolf ● Christopher Claremont & John Bolton
The Amazing Spider-Man in Hooky ● Susan K. Putney &
Berni Wrightson
Doctor Strange—Into Shamballa ● J.M. DeMatteis & Dan Green
Daredevil: Love & War ● Frank Miller & Bill Sienkiewicz

published by
THE MARVEL COMICS GROUP
387 Park Avenue South
New York, NY 10016
second printing

ISBN: 0-87135-171-4

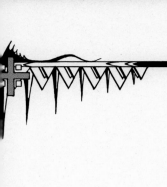
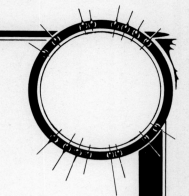

TO JEFFREY JONES

in admiration and affection
and in memory of so many conversations
about the possibilities of words and pictures

ACKNOWLEDGMENTS

My special thanks to Marc DeMatteis, Allen Spiegel, and Carol Zaloom, all of whom read the script at various stages and gave invaluable advice and encouragement. I am especially in debt to Ann Nocenti, for making intelligible a skein of ideas and emotions, and for helping to see to it that the dream flows undisturbed. I am also indebted to Margaret Clark, for making the work look loved. Thanks to Milt Schiffman and Daniel Chichester for technical assistance above and beyond the call of duty, and my sincere gratitude to Jim Shooter, for his stalwart patience and belief in the worth of this project.

For striking the initial chord in this symphony I am, of course, beholden to Bram Stoker.

PROLOGUE

"All we see, and all we seem,
are but a dream.
A dream within a dream."

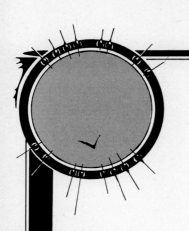

extract from the log of the Demeter;
Twenty men lost to a fever, and four vanished without a trace. Only the mate and I are left. The sea is running mountains high and the wind is a tempest. We are lost and I hold the wheel and pray. The storm seems to move with us and God has abandoned us. All my prayers turn to ashes in my mouth.

DRACULA

Lucy Seward's Diary

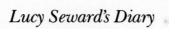

As I write, Mina is watching the sea and sky from our bedroom window. Last night was very threatening, and the fishermen say that we are in for a storm. Mina is more excitable than ever, but is otherwise well. My father has prescribed some laudanum for her.

Last night she woke up screaming and the night before, I found her sleepwalking on the cliffs.

There must be something in the air. Right along with Mina, I too have felt a strangeness. I try to keep my mind on daily things, but I catch myself staring as if hypnotized, out to sea. It sounds preposterous, even to me, but I have the deepest feeling that I'm waiting. Just waiting. Though waiting for whom or what I cannot say.

extract from the log of the Demeter;

> I will carry my principles with me to the bottom, if I must, but I will not abandon the voyage. We must go on for the sake of those poor men who have already died. Man prevails. There is no other law.
>
> ...I am growing weaker, and again the night is coming on. I dare not leave the helm.

> ...so here I stayed, and in the dimness of the night I saw it—**HIM!** God forgive me but the mate was right to jump overboard. The deck about me swarms with death like a flock of blinded birds! The Devil himself has come to court us!

Lucy Seward's Diary

I started awake, as a gust of wind and rain swept over my bed. I had the most overpowering feeling that I was witness to some strange ritual. Mina stood before the open window and looked as if she would actually float out into the storm. I called to her and quickly went to close the window. Mina collapsed to the floor and I knelt to wrap the quilt around her, lest she should suffer from exposure. I saw that she was staring, but it was clear that it wasn't I she saw. Still as asleep as ever, her eyes were as motionless as the moon. Her pretty lips were parted and she was breathing—not softly, as is usual with her, but in heavy gasps, as though striving to fill her lungs. I wondered then if she might be seriously ill.

She has always had an anemic sort of look about her. Her mother, God rest her soul, had the same pale colouring. Mina's face most often shines with good intention. She told me once that she had had a vision of how life went for people who weren't as lucky as she. Lately, I notice, this sweetness has been cast in shadow. She no longer insists on helping the cook bake pine-nut bread nor does she seek me out in the afternoons to bicycle down to the canals and watch the swans come by. And the scarf she has been knitting for her father's visit lays abandoned on her dressing table.

Lucy Seward's Diary

Lightning flashed across Mina's features and I gasped at the beautiful young face made deathly for an instant then swallowed by the dark. As I helped her back to bed, she smiled in a strange way that brought a knot to my stomach but when I saw my own face reflected in the window glass, I nearly cried out! The same distant smile which danced unexplained across Mina's lips rested on my face too!

I couldn't sleep for the longest time. I lay in bed watching the wreaths of sea mist sweep by. At times the mist cleared, and the sea for some distance could be seen in the glare of the lightning, which now came thick and fast, followed by such sudden peals of thunder that the whole sky overhead trembled under the shock of the footsteps of the storm.

The telephone followed by father's voice filling the hallway, woke me the second time. Mrs. Renfield, who wasn't due for another three weeks yet, had gone into labour and father asked for my assistance. He has never been particularly good with nervous people and Mrs. Renfield is most peculiar. I opened the bedroom door and answered that I would be down presently. I hesitated at first to say that I would go with him, thinking of Mina's sleepwalking, but I couldn't send father out to do battle with Mrs. Renfield and the storm by himself.

It is difficult to say for sure, but as I closed the bedroom door behind me, I'd swear I heard Mina's sleeping voice whisper..."His red eyes again..."

cuttings from "The Dailygraph"

... Another good ship has suffered upon our reefs—
apparently due to the great and sudden storm. It
was found by Dr. John Seward and his daughter,
Lucy, as they searched the undercliffs for their
friend and houseguest, Miss Mina Van Helsing,
who was, it seems, walking in her sleep.

The schooner is a Russian one from Varna and is
called the Demeter...

...There were no survivors...

CHAPTER  VI

"...grandest of the angels, and
most wise,
O' fallen god, fate driven
from the skies..."
—Baudelaire

EXTERIOR. SHIPWRECK ON THE UNDERCLIFF. WISMAR.
DAWN. 1886

A large group of men, women, and children, stands behind a police
rope, looking anxiously at the wreckage. A carriage draws up.
JONATHAN HARKER gets out of it and looks about him.

One man crouches in the water, unloading the ship's remains.
Chests on pulleys, stacked at the water's edge. Dray horse with cart
standing by.

JONATHAN makes his way through the crowd.

> CONSTABLE
> **Back please! Everyone just stay clear.**

JONATHAN steps forward.

> CONSTABLE
> **Yuv' no business down there, have ye now?**

> JONATHAN
> **I'm looking for Dr. Seward.**

Calling past the officer.

> JONATHAN
> **Doctor!**

DR. JOHN SEWARD, dressed in a dark great-coat, and carrying a
medical bag. He stands on a broad sloping ledge of grass, staring at
the shipwreck below. Without turning, he motions for JONATHAN
to join him.

JONATHAN
**Lucy said you would be here. Quite a storm
last night eh, Doctor?**

Pause.

JONATHAN
**I hope Mina's all right. I heard she was out
adventuring.**

SEWARD
Look Jonathan. Look there.

JONATHAN follows his gaze.

JONATHAN
Renfield?

SEWARD
**Yes. Renfield. I sat with that man's wife for five
hours while she gave birth last night, and he
wasn't there for a minute of it! 'Said she hadn't
seen him at all yesterday and, by God, I don't
believe he's been home yet! Like a man
possessed, he's pullin' those damn crates outta
the water...**

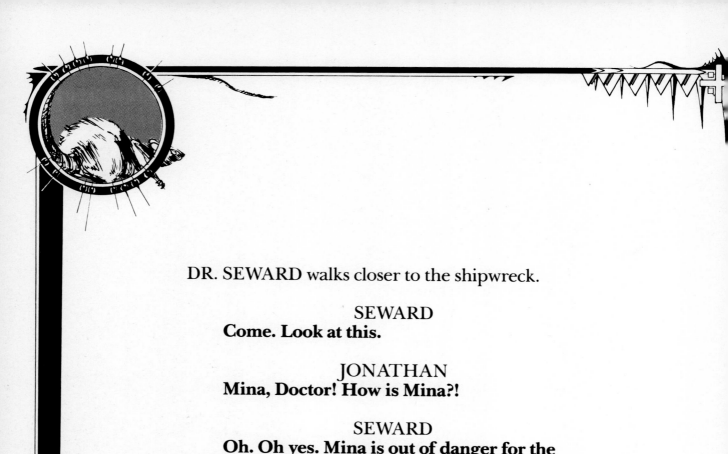

DR. SEWARD walks closer to the shipwreck.

SEWARD
Come. Look at this.

JONATHAN
Mina, Doctor! How is Mina?!

SEWARD
Oh. Oh yes. Mina is out of danger for the moment. As weak as water and pale beyond my liking, but, she is always pale beyond my liking.

DR. SEWARD stops at the edge of the Undercliff. He looks down sharply.

SEWARD
Mina will be all right. But not this poor man.

JONATHAN
Good Lord!! His throat...

SEWARD
**Mmm...It baffles me. He has been attacked
repeatedly...but he doesn't appear to have
struggled. There's not another soul on board.
Very strange.**

Pause.

SEWARD
**They found the log. Russian. The last few pages
filled with some kind of strange symbols.**

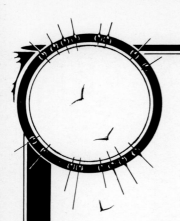

DR. SEWARD turns and walks up the ledge.

JONATHAN stares at the dead man.

> SEWARD
>
> **Mr. Renfield! Where are you going with all of
> this?**

RENFIELD, carrying his load up to the wagon, doesn't break stride,
calls over his shoulder.

> RENFIELD
>
> **Ah've got ter take it t' Carfax. Ta owner 'ill be
> needin' 's things now won't 'e? Ay, an' 'e don't
> need me messin' abaht. Ah've got ter be seein'
> after 'em, ain' ah?**

> SEWARD
>
> **Can't it wait? You should go home, man—and
> see after your wife!**

> RENFIELD
>
> **Oh, nossir. It canna wait. Ye see Doct'r, ta
> sun'll be goin' down soon.**

LETTER FROM BILLINGTON & SONS SOLICITORS, WHITBY, TO MESSRS. CARTER, WRIGHTSON AND CO., WISMAR

"Dear Sirs,

Herewith please receive invoice of goods sent by sailing vessel, Demeter...We shall be obliged by your having a man ready in Wismar at the time named and forthwith conveying the goods to destination.

...Pray do not take us as exceeding the bounds of business courtesy in pressing you in all ways to use the utmost expedition.

We are, dear Sirs
Faithfully yours,
Samuel F. Billington & Sons."

A sparkle glimpsed in a dark corner.

RENFIELD
What th' Devil?

A fluttering sound as if from great leather wings and then a
voice; first one, then a choir, then one again, calls out:

Imagine...

DRACULA

**All of the things... you've only dreamed of—all
of them yours. I can make you rich Renfield.
Would you like that? Rich beyond belief. You
will see life through the eyes of centuries.
Wealth and power.**

Pause.

DRACULA

**I have seen men live and flourish, and I have
seen men beg to die. I will show you that your
soul, too, is a hunter.**

RENFIELD backs away against the wall. The room grows darker.

DRACULA

**But...you must help me now. I have spent a long
time searching...Now something draws me to
this little grey town. I have a wild hunger...to
know everything about it.**

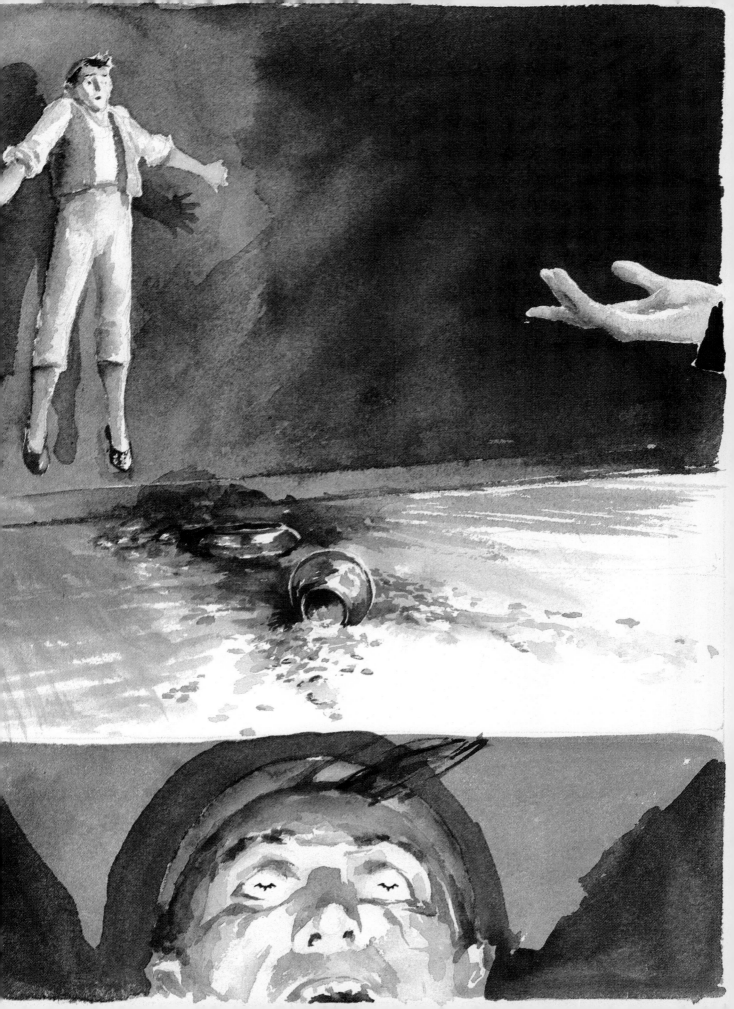

INTERIOR. THE SEWARD MANSION. MINA'S ROOM. DUSK.

Lucy stands looking out the window.

> LUCY
> **What dress shall I wear?**

> MINA
> **It doesn't matter.**

> LUCY
> **What do you mean it doesn't matter? Of course it matters. We don't want this viscount, or whatever he is, thinking that we're all backward here. After all, we don't often have dinner guests. You should be excited.**

> LUCY
> Pause.
> **Father says he is from Romania...or was it Hungary?**

                    MINA
Who?

                    LUCY
Dracula.

                    MINA
You should wear your blue dress. He would like
you in your blue.

                    LUCY
It seems that ship you found the other night was
carrying his belongings.

                    MINA
Yes.

                    LUCY
And he wants to thank you.

                    MINA
Yes.

                    LUCY
Mina, what is the matter with you?

MINA smiles.

                    MINA
Nothing...shall I wear these shoes?

At the head of the table sat a large black shadow. 'If he had a tail', Mina thought, holding the napkin over her mouth to stifle a giggle, 'it would be twitching.'

A cat invited to dinner by a family of mice.

"If you don't eat something, young lady, you'll waste away." Dr. Seward said gravely, aiming with his fork and stabbing his last pea.

Mina said nothing. She stared instead at the bit of food settling in the doctor's beard.

"Will your wife be joining you, Count?" Dr. Seward asked.

Mina watched the shadow shift its weight in the chair and for a moment saw, in its scales, glints of violet and vermilion. Then she heard it speak.

"No, Dr. Seward," Dracula said, "that is to say, I'm not married."

"Ah well," the doctor nodded and winked, "there is still time."

Ancient diamond eyes watched Lucy returning to the table. "Yes," Dracula said, "there is time."

from the Journal of John Seward M.D.

...Halfway through our delightful dinner with the Count I got a call from Arthur Clumly, next door, asking me to come look at his little boy. Another case of influenza. This year's flu was working its way through town.

I suggested that the Count stay, as it should only keep me away for a few minutes, and the girls were *so* looking forward to his visit. It would be a shame to cut it short. He agreed to keep them company the few minutes I would be gone—a very kind gentleman, if a trifle shy and somewhat lifeless, but by no means poor company...

...Upon returning I found Lucy had had a faint, and the Count, apparently in an attempt to revive her, was kneeling over her, whispering in her ear.

Mina found all of this funny in the extreme. The Count—poor devil—it must have given him a start because he left in a fluster with barely a word. I can't blame him though, not being married or used to feminine frailties; the sight of a young woman fainting could be upsetting. The blue-bloods are so often skittish...

Lucy Seward's Diary

I came back to consciousness on the couch. Little by little I remembered what had happened, and I heard, as if in dim memory, the howl of the wind, lifting curtains, whistling through hallways, and snuffing out candles and oil lamps. As consciousness brightened, I came to understand that the wind was actually a voice, a girl's voice. It had been going, like a voice in a dream for sometime. It sharpened now, and I could hear that it was laughter. Then there seemed to be another voice, a man's. I was aware, at first, only of red, red hair, sweeping out like some ludicrous halo around a pale white face.

Mina sat opposite me on the other couch, clutching her doll, her head tipped back, roaring with laughter. She tried to say something but the laughing only got worse.

A sharp pain went up my sinus passage and I recognized it in a moment: smelling salts. Father's voice said clearly, "She's reviving now."

Mina cackled so hard a brilliant tear rolled down her cheek. Suddenly father's voice boomed "Mina, will you please control yourself!"

She choked with laughter, holding the doll up to cover her mouth. And still she couldn't stop. Then in a flash of sharp teeth she bit down deeply into the doll's neck.

CHAPTER  II

"Why do your locks and
rumpled clothes show
'Tis more than usual sleep has
made them so?
Why are the kisses which he
gave betrayed,
By the impression which his
teeth have made?"
—Ovid

The old man sat staring out the train window. Whistles blew and the train trembled into motion. Everything outside was grey; the trees, the clouds, the sky even the departing sunlight.

If only I could sleep, he thought with longing, I could think more clearly.

In the rush of images passing him through the steam, the telegraph poles sailing by, tall ugly villas, alleys with stagnant water radiant for a moment with grey liquid light, one detail stood out plain: a pretty young girl, standing in the shallow dingy recess of a doorway. The wind pulled at her untamed red hair and she smiled at him, eyes flashing, as the blood ran out of her mouth.

Then darkness fell outside as the train entered a tunnel and the old man could see only the transparent reflections of his own terrified features.

His spine was icy and his throat was dry.

He squeezed his hand more tightly around the tiny gold locket and a tear welled up and rolled down his face.

LUCY
I know it's late...But I wanted to come...and
thank you personally for sending the flowers.

DRACULA
It was all very sudden. I'm sure you will miss
her. I was away when I heard the news otherwise
I would have been there myself.

LUCY
Oh, yes. The service was lovely. The whole
town had gathered.

Pause.

DRACULA
I would hope that...you don't mourn for
her...unduly.

She looked at him. She felt a warmth rising in her. The light from the unshaded lantern was merciless. But the glare had no effect on him. A cool dark face which didn't ask for anything, which simply existed, waiting—it was an empty face, she thought; a face that could change with any wind of expression. One could dream into it anything. Like a beautiful, empty house waiting for carpets and pictures. It had all possibilities—it could become a palace or a brothel. It depended on the one who filled it. How limited by comparison was all that is already completed and labeled.

                    DRACULA
        **I'm glad that you came. Your father let you come
        through the woods alone?**

                    LUCY
        **He is away. He has gone to meet Mina's father at
        the train station.**

Pause.

                    LUCY
        And...

She traces the back of a chair with her finger.

                    LUCY
        I didn't tell him that I was going out.

His eyes gleamed in the light from the lamp; one could look right through them and see no end.

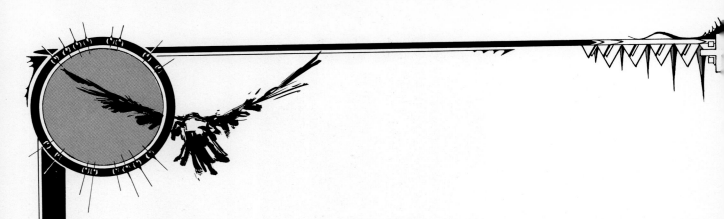

A wave of nausea swept over her. And for a moment blackness tinged the edges of Lucy's vision. The journey through the forest had given her a chill that penetrated her bones.

She grabbed the edge of the table for support. Suddenly the room was darker. Shadows had fluttered in and crouched in the corners.

Those eyes, Lucy thought. As if behind them lightning were flashing. Soft reddish lightning out of a thunderstorm of candles.

She sank to one knee. Now he was supporting her.

His face was so close, now above hers, that in this moment it blotted out all the rest of the world for her. She looked at it. It was a landscape that she knew and did not know, very strange and very familiar, always the same and never the same. She saw it and knew that it was she who had made it mysterious, she knew that there were better faces, purer faces—but she knew too that this face, like no other, had power over her. And she herself had given it this power. She felt the ebb and flow of his breath. Invisibly and tenderly, it was vibrating toward her, without weight, ready and full of reassurance—a strange life in a strange night. Suddenly she felt his blood. It mounted and mounted and it was more that that: life, a thousand times cursed and welcome, often lost and rewon—an hour ago still a barren hillside, arid, full of sharp rocks, painful loss, and without consolation—and now gushing, gushing as if from many fountains, resounding and close to the mysterious moment when one could believe, this soft golden confusion flooding one's brain.

She felt something open up in her and spread; warm and soft and wide, something that drew her down as though with many hands, and made it suddenly unbearable that they were side by side absurdly upright, balancing, instead of forgetting and sinking down, yielding to the call of the skin, the call behind the millenniums when there did not as yet exist brains and thoughts and suffering and doubt, but only the dark happiness of the blood—question and answer in one. It mounted and mounted, and a storm began above her eyes.

"Hold me," she said.

CHAPTER  III

"...in a nightmare without
cease
you dream of poison to bring
peace..."
—Rodenbach

The old man sits down, removes his hat, and runs a hand through his thinning hair. His hands are shaking. The old man's eyes are on fire and black as dinosaur bones.

                    MINA
          Papa, I've done...questionable things.

                 VAN HELSING
          **Yes, I know, Mina. The Lord has shown me.
          Shown me in wonderous visions. I have seen. I
          too, was a sinner, but He has given me faith. He
          has shown me The Way. He has restored me. He
          has shown me the wild work that must be done,
          and He can help you too.**

VAN HELSING takes MINA's hand.

                 VAN HELSING
          **Let's pray together, Mina. You and I. Let's get
          down on our knees and ask the Lord's forgiveness.**

                    MINA
          The Lord?

She asks as if she cannot place the name.

                 VAN HELSING
          **"The Lord is my shepherd, I shall
          not want..."**

MINA
The Lord is so far from us now, He cannot hear
a word...

VAN HELSING
"He maketh me to lie down in green pastures..."

MINA
The sound of the tempest drowns us out.

VAN HELSING
"He leadeth me beside the still waters..."

MINA
But I do not blame Him. He has had
to bear so much evil.

VAN HELSING
"He restoreth my soul..."

MINA
I think...

e closes her eyes, smiling.

MINA
...He is quite as alone as we are now.

Renfield stands in the bell tower window with a terrible thrill in his heart, watching dark birds circle in the sky overhead, as if waiting for some holy procession. The huge stone angel that towers over Wismar Square looks down across the town at him, full of love and awe.

"'E's taken 'is church and 'e's left from this place!" Renfield yells down, looking crafty, "You'll never find 'im now!". He pauses, head cocked, as if afraid he might have started something. No response. He moans loudly and stamps his feet on the grey-stone sill. His tear-filled eyes grow darker, fuliginous. Then he laughs, a single irate snort as if he has glimpsed for an instant something suddenly obvious . . .

. . . and he throws himself out into the air.

Message left at Wismar Train Station for Abraham Van Helsing:

Very sorry I couldn't meet you. There's been an accident at the church in town. Please make your way to our house and rest.

John Seward

Writings found in the margins of a bible, taken from the person of A. Van Helsing

Was it merely my imagination that the sky had gone darker, lost luster... No. It was a sign.

The night was sullen and overcast. My horse was irritable, indignant, but I drove him cruelly, forgetting all good will, never permitting him to slack, old and weary as he was. His hooves rang out in the abandoned darkness. He got his second wind; his mane and tail streamed out like those of a younger or infinitely older horse, the terrible black the Devil drives.

There was power crackling in the air. Dark power. Enough to shake the world to bits. My spirit shrank, every ember of Chrisitianity flaring up in alarm. I was on the right track.

Writings found in the margins of a bible, taken from the person of A. Van Helsing

I thought for a moment of the old woman. The one whose cart I am now in, riding through perilous night. How she had looked up at me in alarm. A trick to make me forget myself. I was not fooled. I pierced her heart with the stake twenty times and once more for good measure. Her gnarled hand trembled like a tree in high wind, and her cracked demon's face was yellowish green in the moonlight. She gave a moan, a kind of wail with words in it, jumbled, then helplessly tumbling. Another of the Devil's own sent to perdition. Gruesome outcasts, sharp-toothed fiends in human shape!

I see now that I was put on earth to save the innocent, the children—the flesh and blood lambs of God. "I am coming Lucy! I will not let you be cruelly resurrected. Not like my Mina!"

I swore at the night.

Where the road went under trees, the night was so dark I had nothing to tell me the horse was still there but the clatter of the gig that stiffly, clumsily connected us.

My mind was full of wind, reeling and shrieking, and in the unnaturally-perfect darkness ahead, I saw something even darker...

In the center of the room there is a coffin. In the absolute darkness within, she lays wrapped around him.

> DRACULA
> **He is still coming.**

> LUCY
> **Why doesn't he just leave us alone?**

> DRACULA
> **He's mad. He can't help himself.**

Pause.

> DRACULA
> **Now I will wait for him.**

> LUCY
> **What will you do?**

> DRACULA
> **Shhh. Fall asleep. When you rise the world will
> be new to you.**

Razor sharp teeth touch flesh and she feels herself falling, but not into sleep.

Last Testament of Lucy Seward

They exhanged looks swifter than lightning bolts, and my love's lips parted and stretched back in a grin. His suddenly monsterous teeth flashed. For no reason that I can explain, even now, a shock of terror went through me, blasted like a deep-laid dynamite charge from my spine to my brain. The world was howling now, everything was churning, screaming, writhing, obscured to the vagueness of things seen underwater or things wrapped in fire.

The rest is confused, but I saw what I saw and that is where the world righted itself again. Claws ripped and tore and blood exploded into the room, hot and coppery. Dracula's eyes glowed, triumphant. With every new blow the whole house cracked and shuddered and as the poor professor's head finally fell from his destroyed neck, my nightmare trance melted away, sanity bubbling to the surface. Then, seeing the blood splashed all over my dress, Dracula shrank back, eyes widened, like a terrified horse.

The pounding of my heart was dangerous, and I gasped for air. I glanced at him and his violent history swarmed around him like angry hornets. He stood calm, panting, as the storm of his existence made itself clear to me. I saw all of the undead for a thousand years, reaching out from beneath his cloak, pleading —with groping fingers, mouths gaping like open graves—all calling my name in dreadful chorus.

He looked at me. I was a landscape that he knew and could never know—strange and familiar at the same time—in the same breath. He knew that my face, like no other, had power over him. And he himself had given me this power.

My heart held a kind of calm usually felt only during Bendiction at High Mass. It was all clear—I knew what to do.

Lightning flashed in his cloak as he glided toward me.

"Hold me," he said.

I held him until a cock crowed in the morning air and he made as if to rise, by instinct only. A ray of sun streaked in and he cried out. We were so entwined, so locked in a single fate, that there ceased to be any difference between his pain and mine.

I felt his death tremor, his violent jerking as he fought his way to another world, sunlight piercing him like spears. His eyes were great with sorrow as if he had somehow failed me. I released him and in purple-green light I watched him cringe one last time and die, released from an ages old prison.

Sunlight is all around. Like a cathedral. It gets harder to write. I lay here listening to the uneven thunder of my heart. This huge room around me echoes from window to window, beam to beam. My head throbs and my body aches when I try to move. I feel a numbness in my throat.

Father, I will miss you.

I see my soul spread its wings in the darkness, rising out of the nightmare like herons off a marsh.

I am sober, as still as midnight, full of joy.

$7.95
CAN $10.95

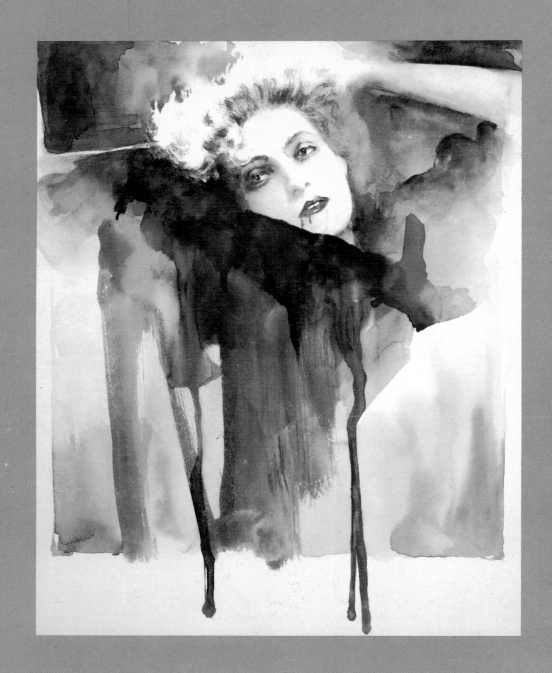

Therefore with the same necessit
with which the stone falls to the
earth, the hungry wolf buries its
fangs in the flesh of its prey, witho
the possibility of the knowledge
that it is itself the destroyed
as well as the destroyer.
—Schopen

ISBN: 0-87135-171-4